all at sea

ℛℛ
RAVETTE BOOKS

This edition first published by Ravette Books Limited 1990

Printed and Bound
for Ravette Books Limited,
3 Glenside Estate, Star Road, Partridge Green,
Horsham, West Sussex RH13 8RA
by Cox & Wyman Ltd, Reading

ISBN: 1 85304 306 0

HAMLET   LUCKY EDDIE   HÄGAR   HELGA   SNERT   HONI

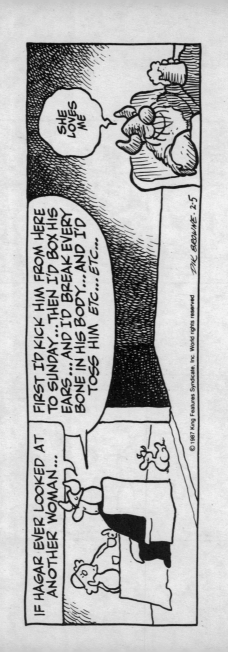

A selection of HÄGAR books published by Ravette

POCKET BOOKS		COLOUR LANDSCAPES	
TRIES AGAIN	£2.25	TELLS IT LIKE IT IS	£2.95
HAS A GO	£2.25	NEVER SAY DIE	£2.95
IN A FIX	£2.25	MAKES AN ENTRANCE	£2.95
ON THE RAMPAGE	£2.25	WELCOME HOME	£2.95
GETS IT ALL	£2.25		
IN THE ROUGH	£2.25	COLOUR THEME BOOKS	
LEADS THE WAY	£2.25	No. 1 THE GREAT GOURMET	£2.95
TAKES A BREAK	£2.25	No. 2 TROUBLE AND STRIFE	£2.95
ON HOLIDAY	£2.25	No. 3 TAKES A JOURNEY	£2.95
TAKES AIM	£2.25	No. 4 CHILD'S PLAY	£3.50
IN A STEW	£2.25	No. 5 WHO DARES WINS	£3.50
MEASURE FOR MEASURE	£2.25		
SAYS IT WITH FLOWERS	£2.25	VIKING HANDBOOK	£3.95

ALBUMS	
THE HERO	£2.50
LETS HIMSELF GO	£2.50

BLACK AND WHITE LANDSCAPES	
MEETS HIS MATCH	£2.50
IN A HURRY	£2.50

All these books are available at your local bookshop or newsagent, or can be ordered direct from the publisher. Just tick the titles you require and fill in the form below. Prices and availability subject to change without notice.

Ravette Books Limited, 3 Glenside Estate, Star Road, Partridge Green, Horsham, West Sussex RH13 8RA

Please send a cheque or postal order and allow the following for postage and packing. UK: Pocket books – 45p for one book plus 20p for the second book and 15p for each additional book. Landscape series – 50p for one book plus 30p for each additional book. Other titles – 85p for one book plus 60p for each additional book.

Name ....

Address ....

....